P9-BZQ-812

The World of Rod McKuen

Books by Rod McKuen

Stanyan Street and Other Sorrows
Listen to the Warm
Lonesome Cities

The World of Rod McKuen

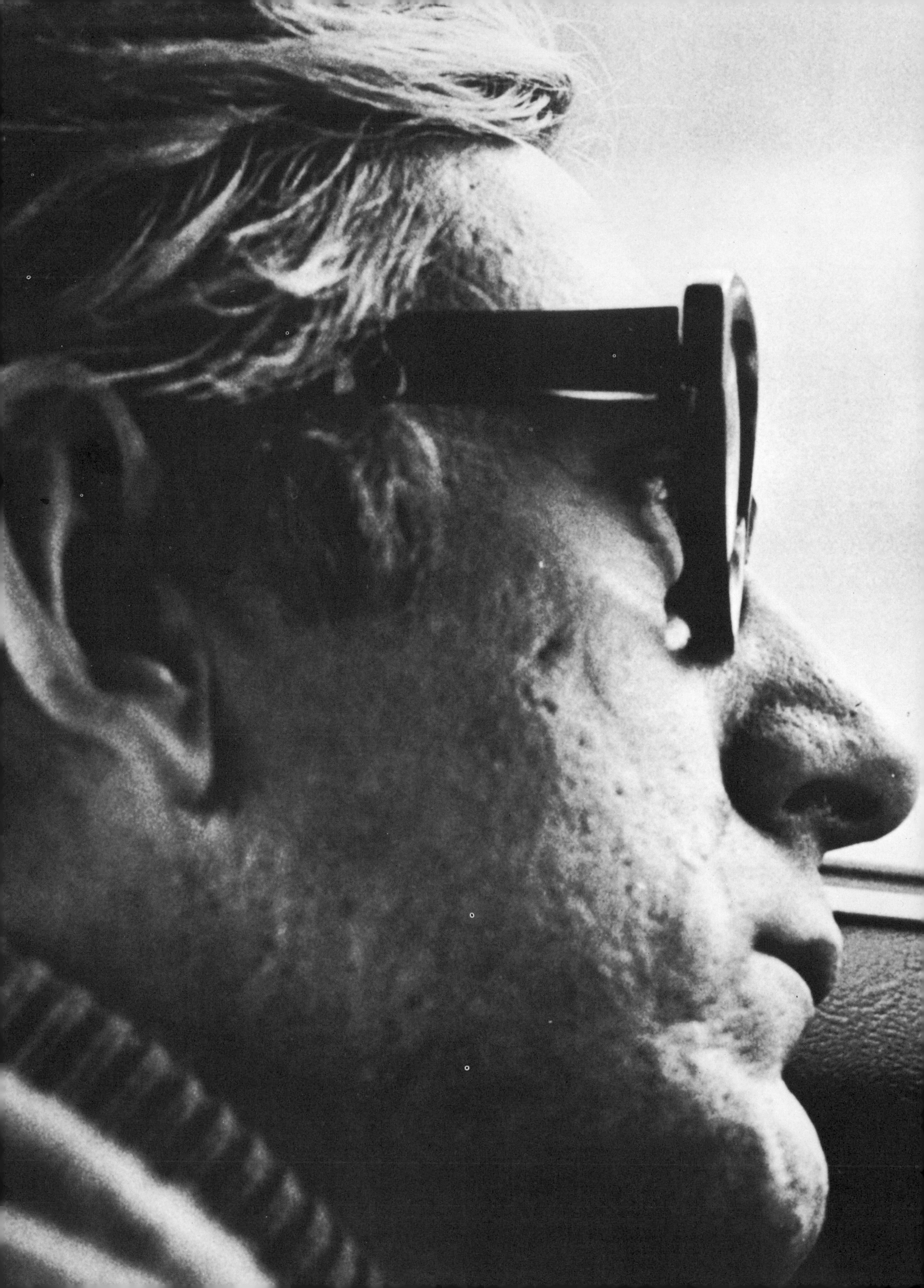

The World of Rod McKuen

Words and Music by Rod McKuen

Photographs by Helen Miljakovich

Piano Arrangements by Ben Kendall

Random House New York

First Printing

Published in the United States by Random House, Inc., New York, and
simultaneously in Canada by Random House of Canada Limited, Toronto.

Library of Congress Catalog Card Number: 68-29390
Manufactured in the United States of America

Cover photo by Photo Media Ltd.

Designed by David Paul and Phoebe Rodbart

For Joe Smith

A Note

I write to find out about myself; what makes me turn. I never wanted to be a writer—or planned to be one. I have always been a singer who needed songs that reflected how he felt about himself and his surroundings in order to make his performance of them believable. In desperation I had to write my own material. There just weren't enough songs reflecting *me,* written by other people.

This book contains twenty-two songs—all of them personal, some of them I think are pretty good. Ben Kendall's arrangements have captured the songs as I wanted them to be. The photographs were taken by Helen Miljakovich. She has invaded, perhaps, a bit more of my world than I'd planned. But she's done so with kindness, intelligence and talent.

People ask me what I like to do best—write poetry, songs, sing, whatever. I don't play favorites. My work, if I can call it that, is all I am. What I write and perform is an extension of myself. *The World of Rod McKuen* is limited to what I know and what I continue to find out about myself and the people and places and thoughts that take me out of myself and into the larger world. I'm not very far into that world yet, but I'm a little further along than I was yesterday.

These songs and this book are a gift to those who've been able to make me have a world at all.

Rod McKuen
London, June 1968

Contents

The World of Rod McKuen

Scotch SPOOL 7·18
Scotch

I'm Strong But I Like Roses

F Fm G9 G7(♭9) C B♭
and bid him stay. A man may like ros - es,
C B♭ C B♭ Em Am7
and still be big and strong; And what is life with - out a
F Dm7 G9 C
lit - tle bird's song. I'M STRONG_ BUT I LIKE
B♭ C B♭
ROS - ES And if a bird should come,
8

C Dm7 Em Am Dm7 G7
I'll keep him 'til his sing - ing's all done. I'M
C Bb C
STRONG BUT I LIKE ROS - ES And when he has to
Bb C Dm7 Em
fly, I'll pick an - oth - er rose and watch the
F Dm7(sus) G7 C
days go slow - ly by.

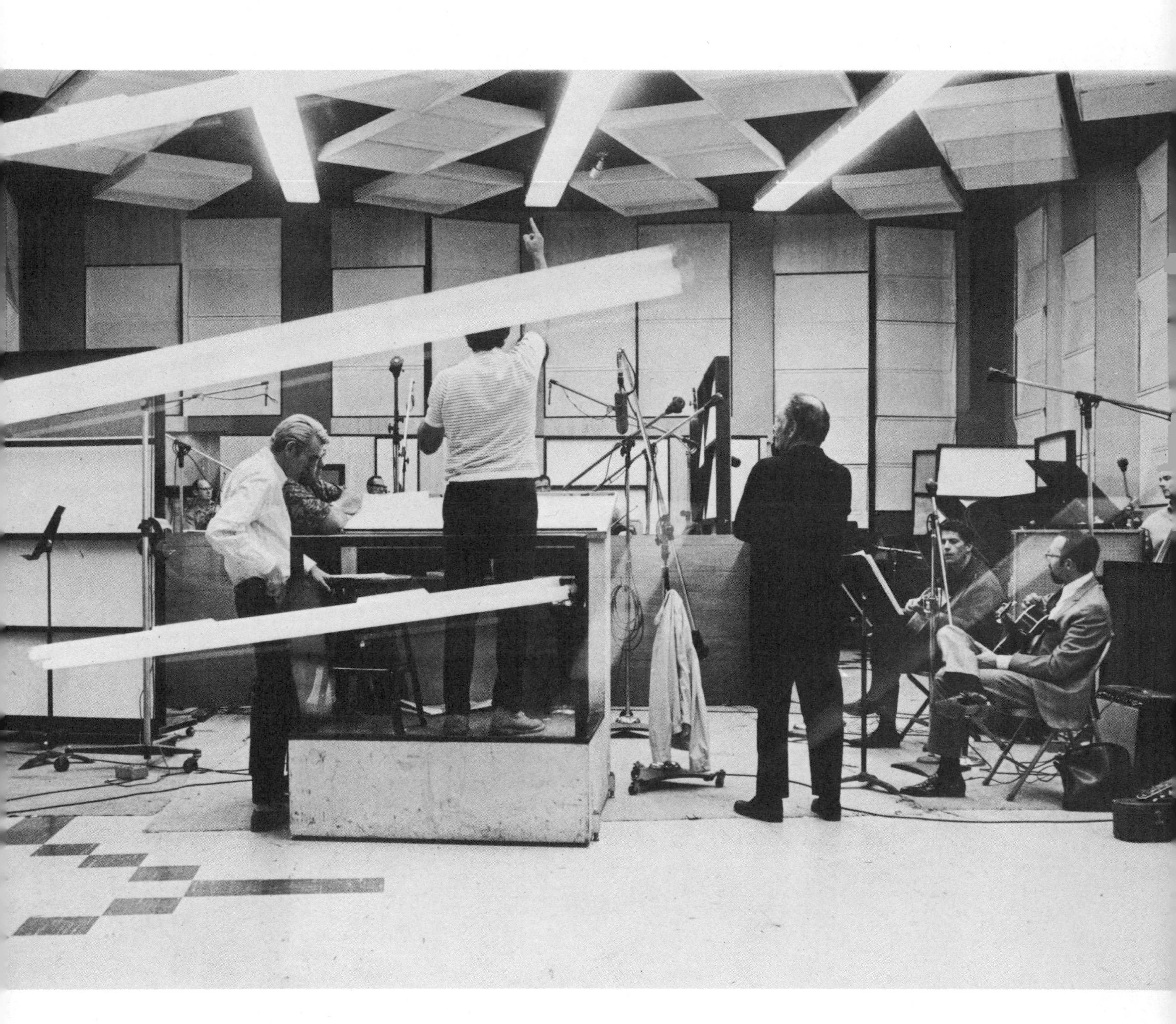

People Change

A
G
D
3
C
blows; Give your love, get heart-break in ex-change, Aft - er
Bb
C
Am
all, PEO-PLE CHANGE. You
G7
C
know as well as I, With just the same old sky,
Em
D
A bird gets might-y rest-less and has to fly.

D
G
D
PEO - PLE CHANGE, Now you're
A
G
A
back, If there's some-thing my old smile seems to lack; I don't
G
C
B♭
love you now, but if you think it strange, Aft - er all, PEO-PLE
G
D
A
G
CHANGE.
a tempo

To Die in Summertime

Dm
si-lence, with-out a sin - gle sound, To touch the earth as gen - tly as a dead leaf, when it
Gm
Dm
hits the ground. To leave be-hind a mem-'ry soft as sum-mer-time, For those one
Gm
Dm
loves and has to leave be - hind. To
Dm
fold as soft - ly as the grass blades fold, When wild things tram-ple them on morn - ings damp and

Gm
Dm
A
cold. To leave be-hind a fra-grance, car-ried on the wind for those one loves and will
Dm
Chorus:
C7
nev-er see a-gain. TO DIE IN SUM-MER-TIME, or not to
mp - mf
F
B♭
C7
F
die at all, While I'm still run-ning, While I'm still run-ning for-ward,
C7
F
While I still own my own mind, I want to go in sum-mer-time.
Dm6(add9)
1.
2.
TO DIE IN

Rod McKuen
The Last of The Wine
Fini

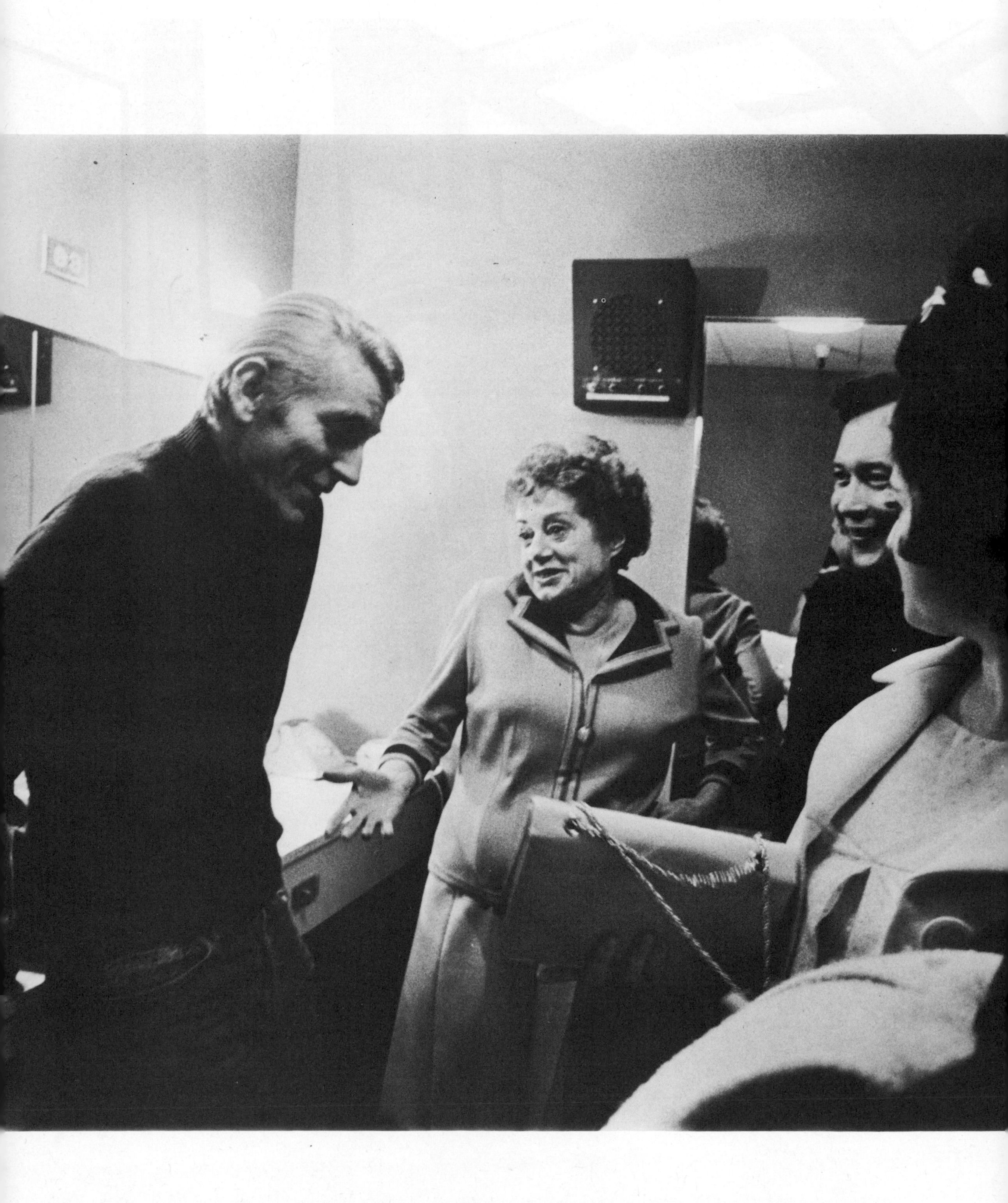

Where Are We Now?

for Charlotte Brennan

Gm7 C7 Fmaj7 Dm7 Gm7 C7 F7 Cm7 F7
WHERE ___ ARE WE NOW? A thou - sand miles a - part.
B♭maj7 B♭6 Am7 Gm7 C7 Fmaj7 F7
What ___ have we now? What have we now?
To Coda
D.S. al Coda
B♭maj7 Am7 Dm Gm7 C9 sus C9 Fmaj7 F6 C9 sus Gm7 C9
Not e - ven love e - nough to break each oth - er's heart.
Coda
C9 sus Gm7 C9 Fmaj7 C11 Fmaj7
We sit with - in the gloom of just this lit - tle room,
Gm7 C7 Fmaj7
Won - der - ing ___ WHERE ARE WE NOW? ___

Love, Let Me Not Hunger

Slowly
Chorus:
D Em7 A7 D Bm7 Em7 A7
LOVE LET ME NOT HUN-GER, I've been a- lone so long;
mf
D G Em7 A7
How can a lit-tle taste of wine be wrong? We'll
D Em7 A7 D Bm7 Em7 A7
not get an-y young-er, Come lis-ten to my song;
D G D A7 D D7
And if you've had a hun-ger, Per-haps you'll sing a-long. The

G
Gm6
D
Em
A7
day's so warm, You can feel the sun,
D
Bm
E7
Em
A7
What does it mat-ter what's done in the day, Aft - er the day is done?
D
Em7
A7
D
Bm7
Em7
A7
LOVE LET ME NOT HUN - GER, Come and take my hand;
D
G
D
A7
D
And if you've ev - er hun - gered, I know you'll un - der - stand.

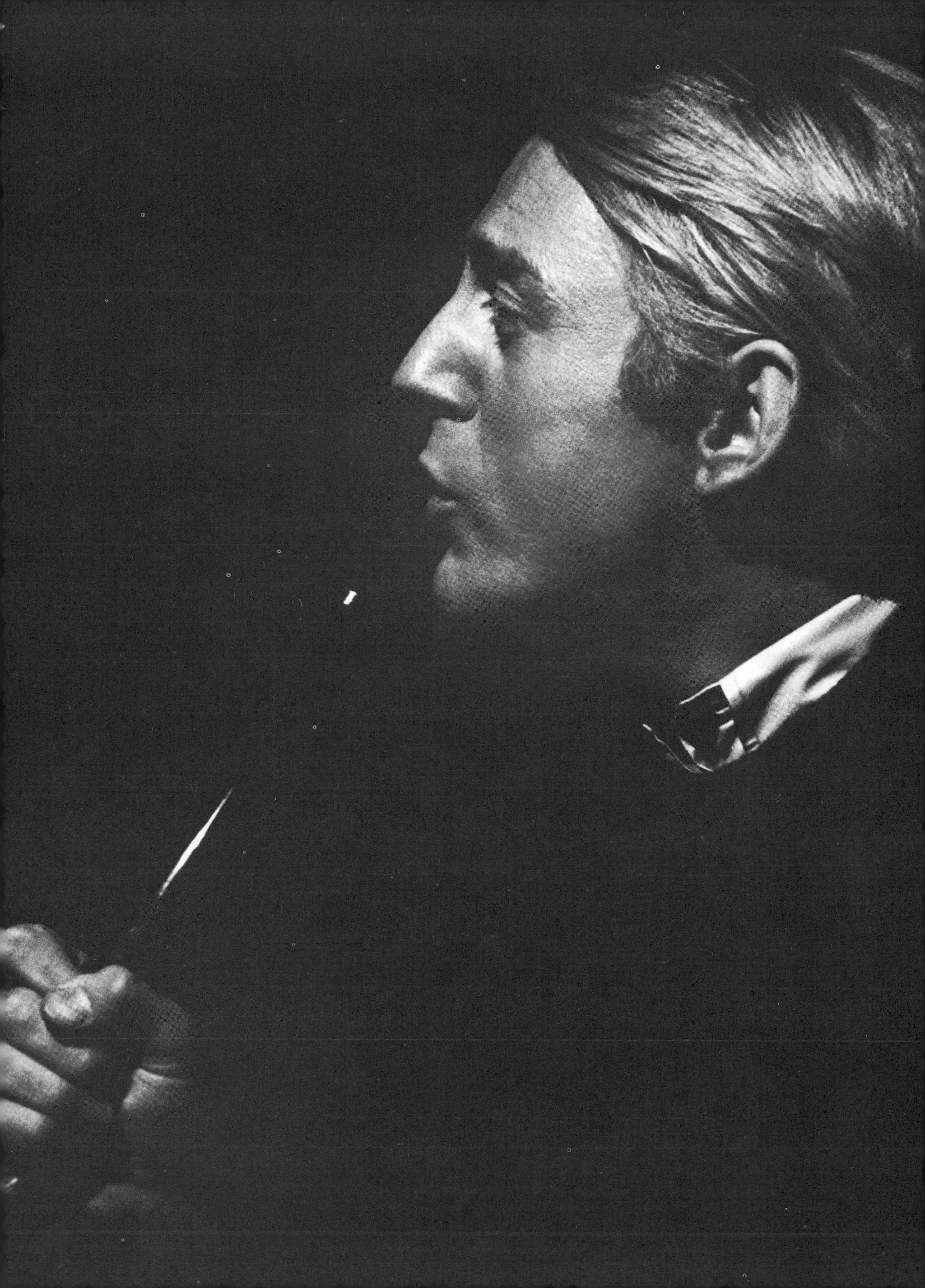

Listen to the Warm

for Phillip and Jeannie Martin

Em7
A7
E9
least, And store up pleas-ures for that rain-y day — When
E♭7(+9)
Dmaj7
Bm
love goes a-way and then Soft, LIS-TEN TO THE WARM, —
C♯m(♭5)
F♯7(+9)
Bm
Bm9
Now the night is gone, — And we can LIS-TEN TO THE
E9
Em7 A13
Dmaj7
D6
WARM. —
Repeat ad lib till fade

The Beautiful Strangers

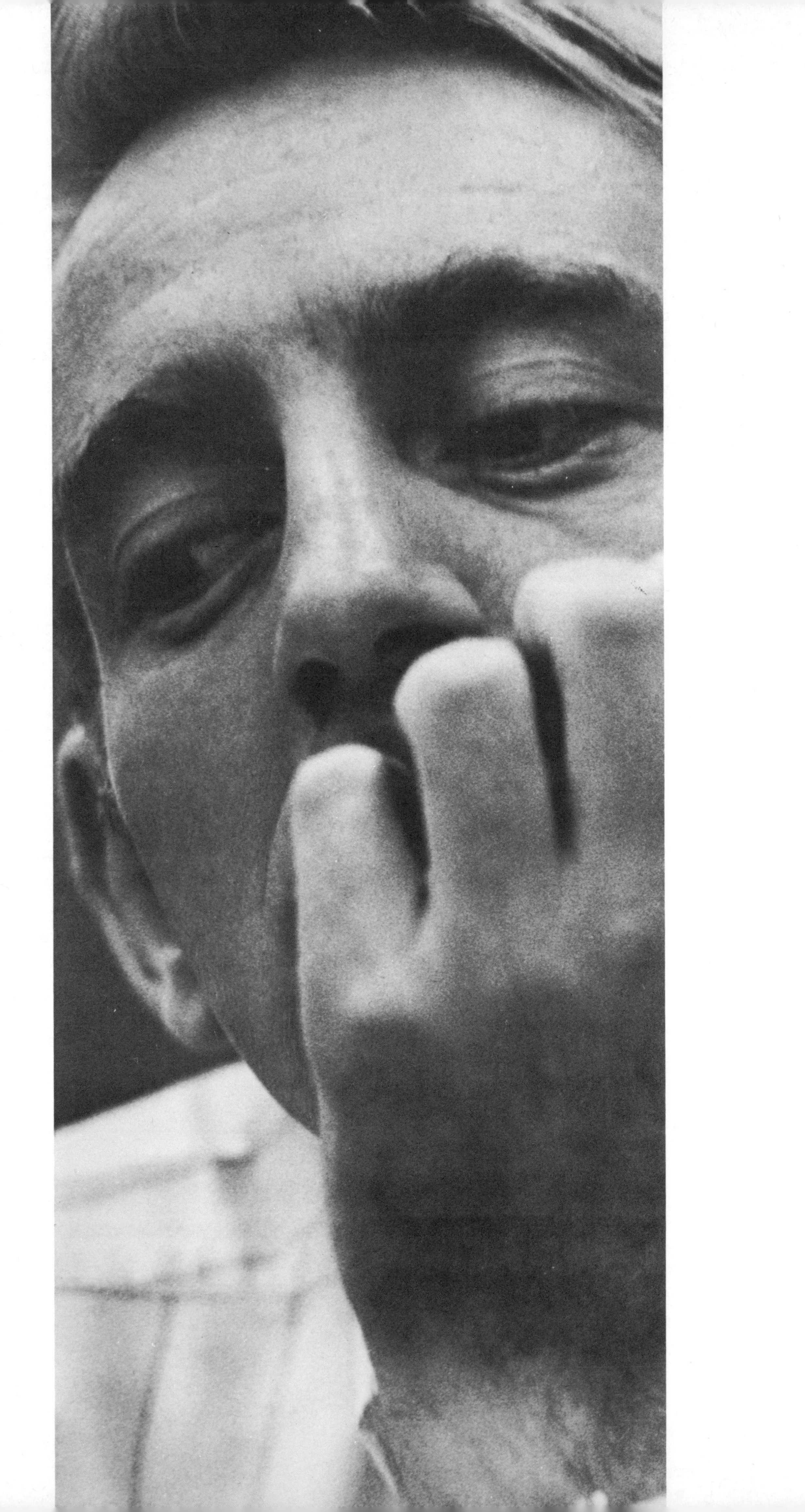

Dm G7 C Am Dm G7
Praised my flat lit - tle stom - ach, And came back to my
C Em
room. ALL THE BEAU - TI - FUL STRAN - GERS
F Bb6 A7 Dm7 G7
Spoiled me for a time; And taught me ne - on's
C Am7 Dm7 G11 C
Just as nice As aft - er - noon sun - shine.
rall.

Looking Back at 30

Cm
Fm
G7
LOOK - ING BACK AT THIR - TY, — one thing time has shown, That's
LOOK - ING BACK AT THIR - TY, it's lat - er than I thought, It's
LOOK - ING BACK AT THIR - TY, and old - er by a mile, There've
LOOK - ING BACK AT THIR - TY, — hold - ing back the tears, I
lit - tle con - so - la - tion, When you spend the day a - lone. But
bad to brood the years a - way for what I have - n't got. For
been too man - y stran - gers, that knew my crook - ed smile. And
might as well be one, — two, — three times thir - ty years. But
mf
1.
Eb
ev - 'ry day's an - oth - er chance, You've got to dance it like it was the fi - nal
dance; And yet a dance is just a dance and noth - ing more, You can't ex-

G7
Cm
pect to turn each turn and find the se - cret door.
2. I
mp
2.
Cm
Eb
Cm
Eb
all you touch you can - not keep, And what is love but just an-
Cm
Eb
Cm
Fm
oth er kind of sleep; And yet to sleep a - gain would be worth all the trou- bles that I've
G7
Cm
G7
Cm
known, Some - time I think I'm nev - er ev - er go - ing home.
3. If I

3.
Cm
Eb
Cm
Eb
oh, the crowds can be so wild, They push and tram-ple you like
Cm
Eb
Cm
Fm
some for-got - ten child; And yet I guess I've nev - er been a child at all,
G7
Cm
Ex - cept some-times in terms of feel - ing small.
4. Some
p
4.
Cm
Eb
Cm
ev - 'ry day's an oth - er dance, You got - ta

Cm
E♭
Cm
dance it like it was the fi - nal dance; And if a
Cm
E♭
Cm
Fm
dance is just a dance and noth - ing more, You've got to
G7
Cm
(tacet)
keep on try - ing hard to find that se - cret door. LOOK-ING BACK AT THIR - TY
ad lib
Cm
That's what liv - ing's for.
a tempo

Love Child

for Robert Fryer
Slowly (freely)
Dm
Dm C Dm
When I was young my ma - ma told me lies, A-
mp
Dm
Dm C Dm
Dm
bout the col - or of my dad - dy's eyes; And how my dad - dy died when I was
Dm C Dm
E♭
A7(♭5)
three. But dad - dy was a lie my ma - ma shared with me. For
Dm
Dm C Dm
E♭
ma - ma's pride has al - ways been as big as her heart, She did - n't want her LOVE CHILD to

GO
A&P
APPLE
SAUCE

Gm
Dm
Dm
know a - bout his start. While I was grow - in' all the kids would
Dm C Dm
Dm C Dm
boast, How their dads was first - est with the most; And
Dm
C Dm
E♭
I told sto - ries too a - bout my dad, The base - ball games and fish - ing trips we
A7(♭5)
Dm
Dm C Dm
had. But I kept play - in' base - ball all a - lone, And a

E♭
Gm
A7(♭5)
Dm
LOVE CHILD — does his fish - in' — in the base-ment at home.
Gm
Dm
C
When I'd ask ques - tions, "Let's not talk a - bout it now.")
That's what ma - ma would
Dm
Gm
Dm
say, "Your dad - dy was a long, — long, — time a - go." And
A7(♭5)
(tacet)
A7
Dm
so I'd — buy her pres-ents ev - 'ry — Fa-ther's Day, And as I grew, I soon for-got the
mp

Dm C Dm
pain, Of hav-ing just my ma-ma's_sec-ond name;
C Dm
And
mf
Dm
from the way she some-times_looks at me,
I
E♭
must be quite a lot like who-
A7(♭5)
ev-er he may be;
Dm
That man who gave his love to her
C Dm
when she was young and wild, And
Dm E♭ Gm
left be-hind a leg-a-cy,
(tacet)
A lit-tle LOVE
Dm Cm Dm
CHILD.
rall.

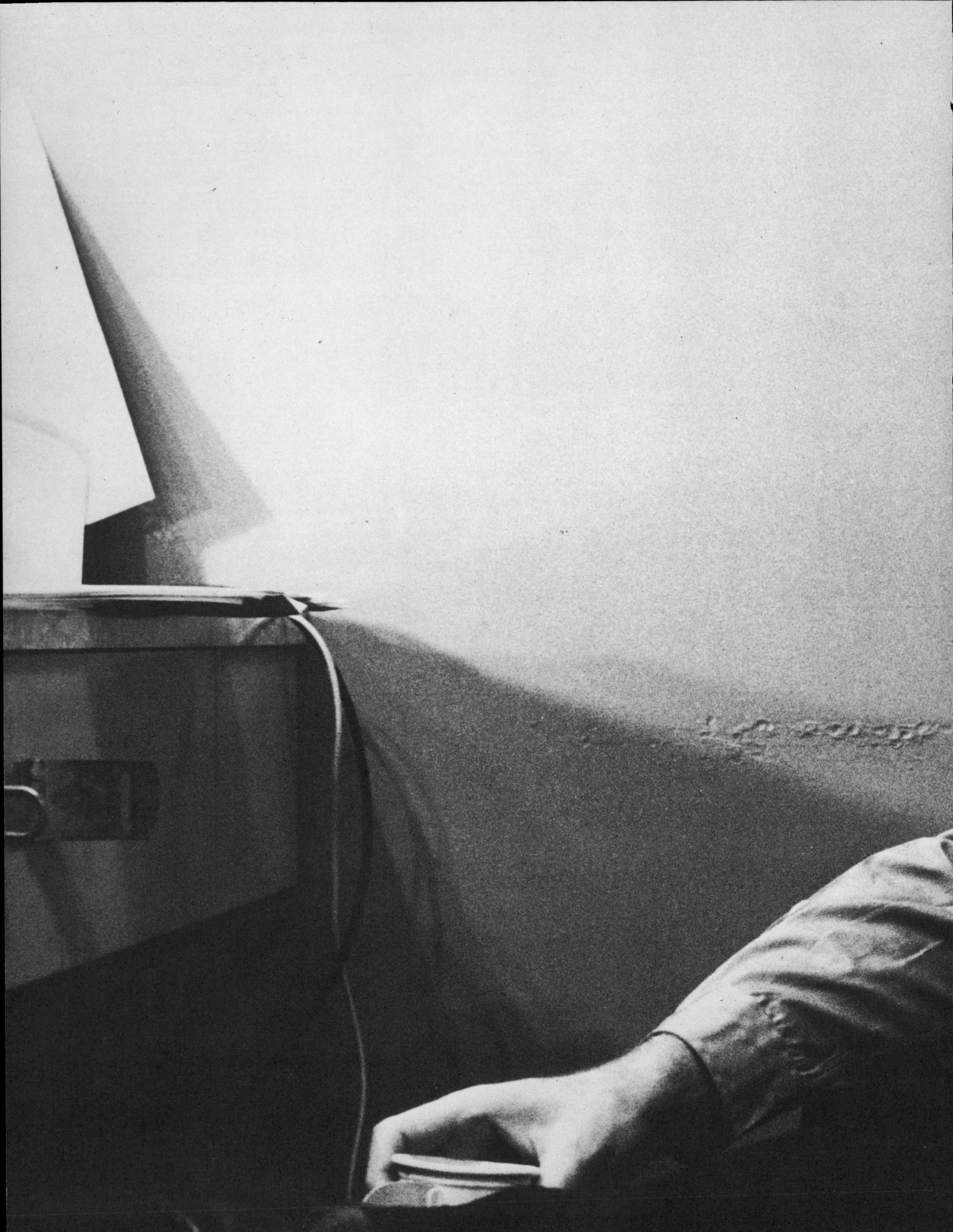

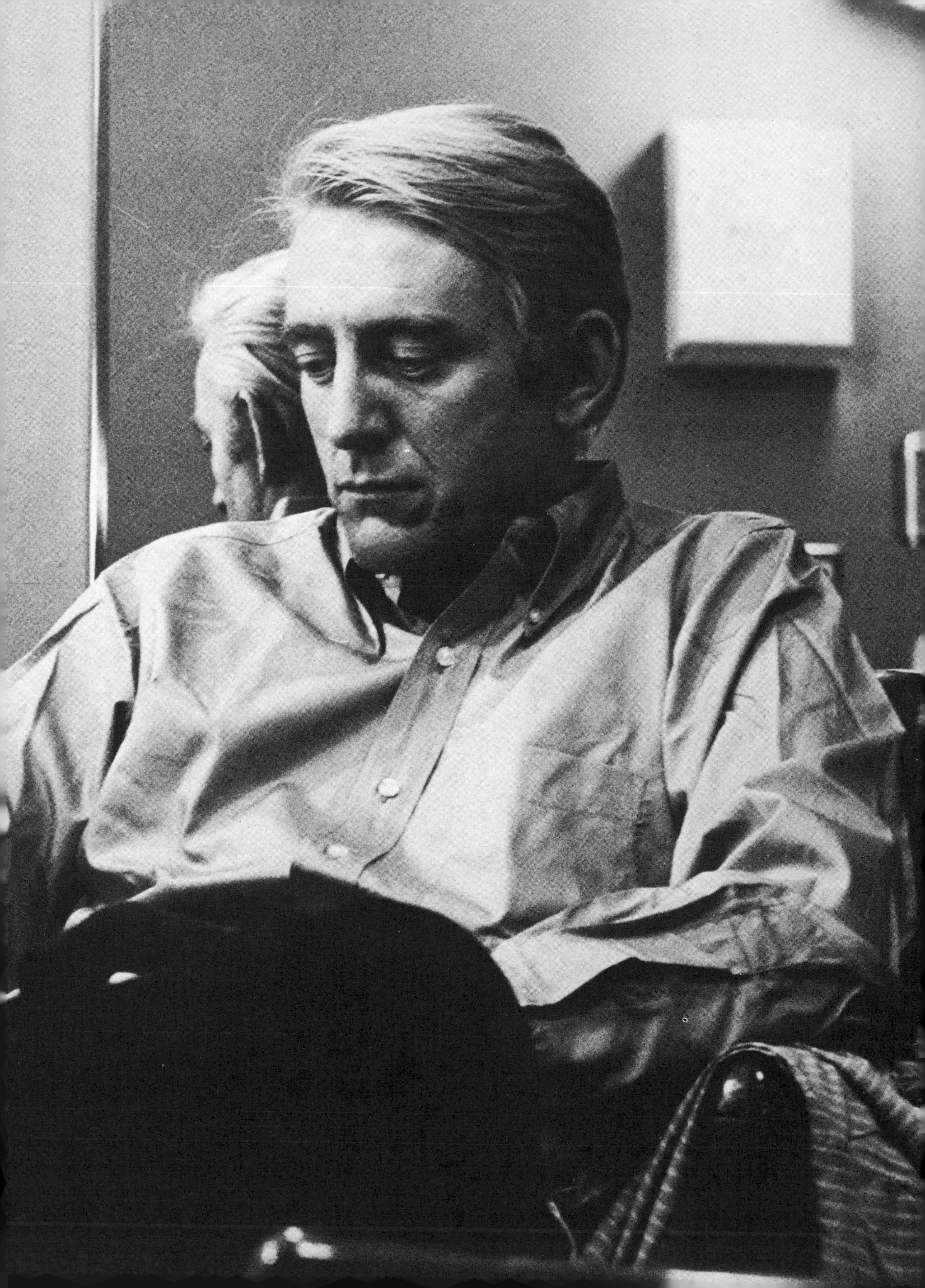

Only Love

Moderato
for Sal and Jo Bonafede
D
Em7
A7
D
1. We have ON - LY LOVE to of - fer as a prayer,
2. We have ON - LY LOVE to help us find our way,
3. We have ON - LY LOVE to keep us free from harm,
mp
Em
Em7
A7
For all the wrongs in the world;
As we go out in - to the world;
As we go a - lone in - to the world;
So
D
G
So like sing - ing trou - ba - dours we'll go.
So like laugh - ing chil - dren we'll go.
on - ly as lov - ers we'll go.

A7
D
Sing - ing love — where - ev - er — we go. — ON - LY
mf

D
Em7
LOVE in an-swer to the can-nons.
ON-LY
A7
D
LOVE in an-swer to the drums;
ON-LY
D7
G
A7
LOVE to-day and the same
When
to-mor-row comes.
1.2.
D
3.
D
comes.

I'll Never Be Alone

F Em C F G7 Em Am7
we'll go gen-tle — in the wood; And what we do for one an-oth-er, —
C F C G7 Cmaj7 Dm7(G) Cmaj7
will be warm and good. I'll wear your love, as one might wear a crown of lau-rel
Dm7(G) Em Em7 A7 Dm7
in his hair. And then if you'll be there, I'LL NEV-ER BE — A-
Bb9 A7(b9) Dm7 Dm7(G) C
LONE, I'll nev-er, ev-er be a - lone. —

RECORDS
rod
mckuen
seasons
in the
sun

PEACE
Johnson Will
To Hawaii Meet
READY TO GO

When Flora Was Mine

Em7 A9 A7(♭9) Dmaj7 3 Bm7 F♯m A7/6
that a - way in the wind; Then home with her arms full of blos-soms and branch-es,
Dmaj7 3 Bm E7 A7 D Em
To wait for the night to be - gin. Now it's win - ter,
F♯m Em A9 D 3 Dmaj7 Em7(11) A7 A7(+5)
We've grown old - er; Me and the dan - de - li - on wine;
D Em F♯m G A Bm7 Em7(11) A7 D
I'm just a fa-ther re - mem-ber-ing the time, When Flo - ra Was Mine.

AIN'T YOU GLAD YOU'RE LIVIN', JOE

D
D7
G
D
E7
clo-ver; On this beach-ball day, if your heart gets in the way, You'll wind up with the
A9
Adim
A7
D
Bm
G
A7
o - cean for a lov - er. Nois - y break - ers wait - in' for the tak - ers,
D
Bm
G
A7
D
Bm
As the wa - ter starts its ebb and flow; Life is like a Sun - day that
G
A7
D
Bm
Em7
A7
D
nev - er knew a Mon - day, And AIN'T YOU GLAD YOU'RE LIV-IN' JOE.

Chasing the Sun

D
Em7
A7
Em7
One of those bright young men,
Run - nin' out
mf
A7
D
aft - er the fun;
To Coda
Em7
One of those bright young men,
(All)
A7
D
CHAS - ING THE SUN.
Coda
A7
D
How pale they all look in the light of the sun.

Gee, It's Nice to Be Alone

Sunday
parade

Em7 A7 Dmaj7 D6 F♯m Bm
chang - ing pan - o - ra - mas, When e - ven the shad - ows don't look
Em7 A7 Dmaj7 G
back at you. Well, GEE IT'S NICE TO BE A - LONE, To find out for your -
A7 Em7 A7 Dmaj7 B7(♭9) G
self, What sol - i - tude's a - bout; And not have a need
Em7 A7 Dmaj7 A7 D
for an - y - bod - y, GEE IT'S NICE TO BE A - LONE some - times.

I Turn to You

Brightly
Gm
F
Gm
mp
1. There are times when I don't know where I'm go - ing,
2. There are times when my friends are less than friend - ly,
3. You with your eyes and arms so ten - der,
Times when I don't know where I'm at; Times when the
Times when my en - e - mies track me down; Times when the
You with your bod - y oh, so warm; You al - ways
world's not round at all, but flat.
cold and chill - y wind comes roar - in' all a - round.
lead me through the wild - est storm.
Times when a day of bright - est
Times when I've had a bad ad-
You with your eyes like thun - der

Gm
F
Gm
sun - shine Seems like the deep - est dark - est night;
ven - ture Times when I feel a - bout to fold;
roar - ing, You with your del - i - cate hands so soft;
F
Gm
Times when no mat - ter what I do, it just don't
Times when the face I face in the mir-ror looks worn and
I've but to stum - ble once on the high - way to have you
turn out right.
tired and old.
car - ry me a - loft.
C
I get lone - some
F
and when I do, I
Gm
TURN TO YOU.
D.C.
D.C.
86

The Loner

With drive
Bm
A
Bm
1. I have rid - den rods and bump - ers, Hitched from New York
2. Been as hun - gry as the wind is, Been as thirst - y
3. I have heard the mad mob rag - ing, Lis - tened as they
mp
A
F#7
Bm
A
Bm
to L. A., Up from Hous - ton in Oc - to - ber, De-
as the dust; One good rain in Am - a - ril - lo,
told their lies; Seen a doz - en lone - some cit - ies,
A
Bm
G
cem - ber down in San - ta Fe. I have walked a hun - dred high - ways
Al - most turned my bones to rust. I have known both light and dark - ness,
Where the sun blacked out the skies. Twen - ty years I've been a Lon - er,

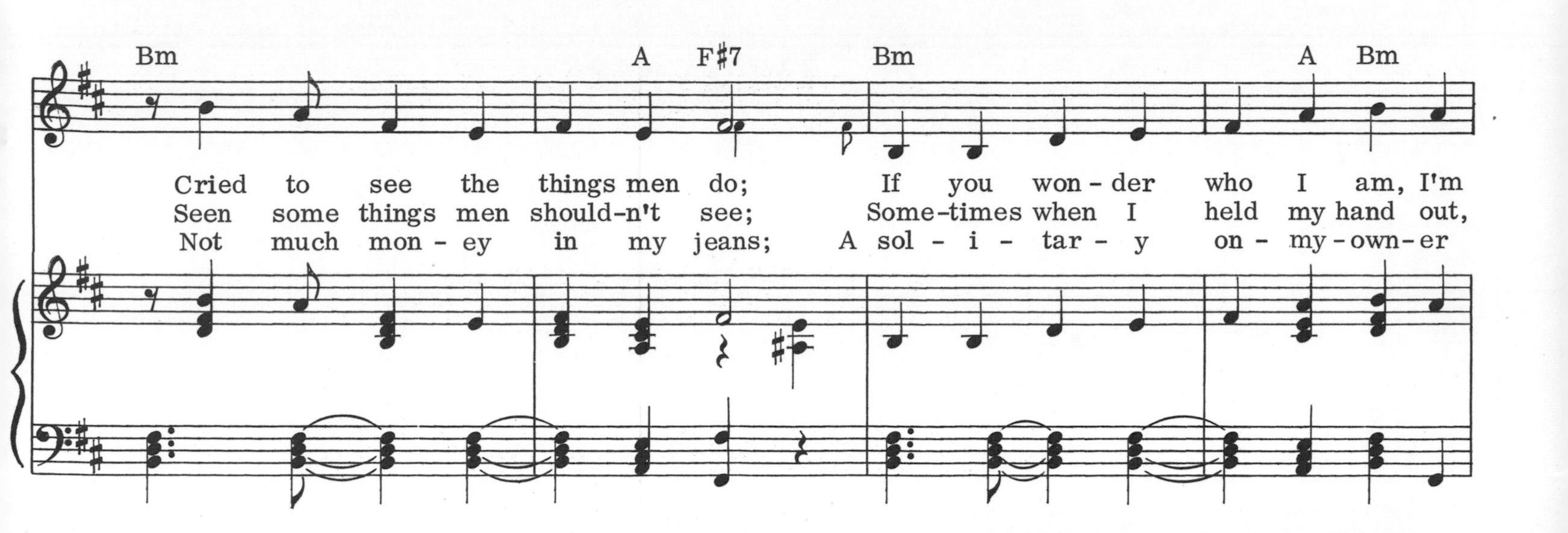
Bm A F#7 Bm A Bm
Cried to see the things men do; If you won-der who I am, I'm
Seen some things men should-n't see; Some-times when I held my hand out,
Not much mon-ey in my jeans; A sol-i-tar-y on-my-own-er

tacet.
Bm
A Bm
Just a Lon - er pass - ing through.
Peo - ple turned their backs on me.
Guess I know what lone - some means.
Chorus
G
Bm
mf
You know me, mis - ter, the man with the old suit-
G
case; You know me, sis - ter, I've
Bm
F#7
3
A Bm D.C.
been ev - 'ry - where, Ain't go - in' no - place.
D.C.
Fine

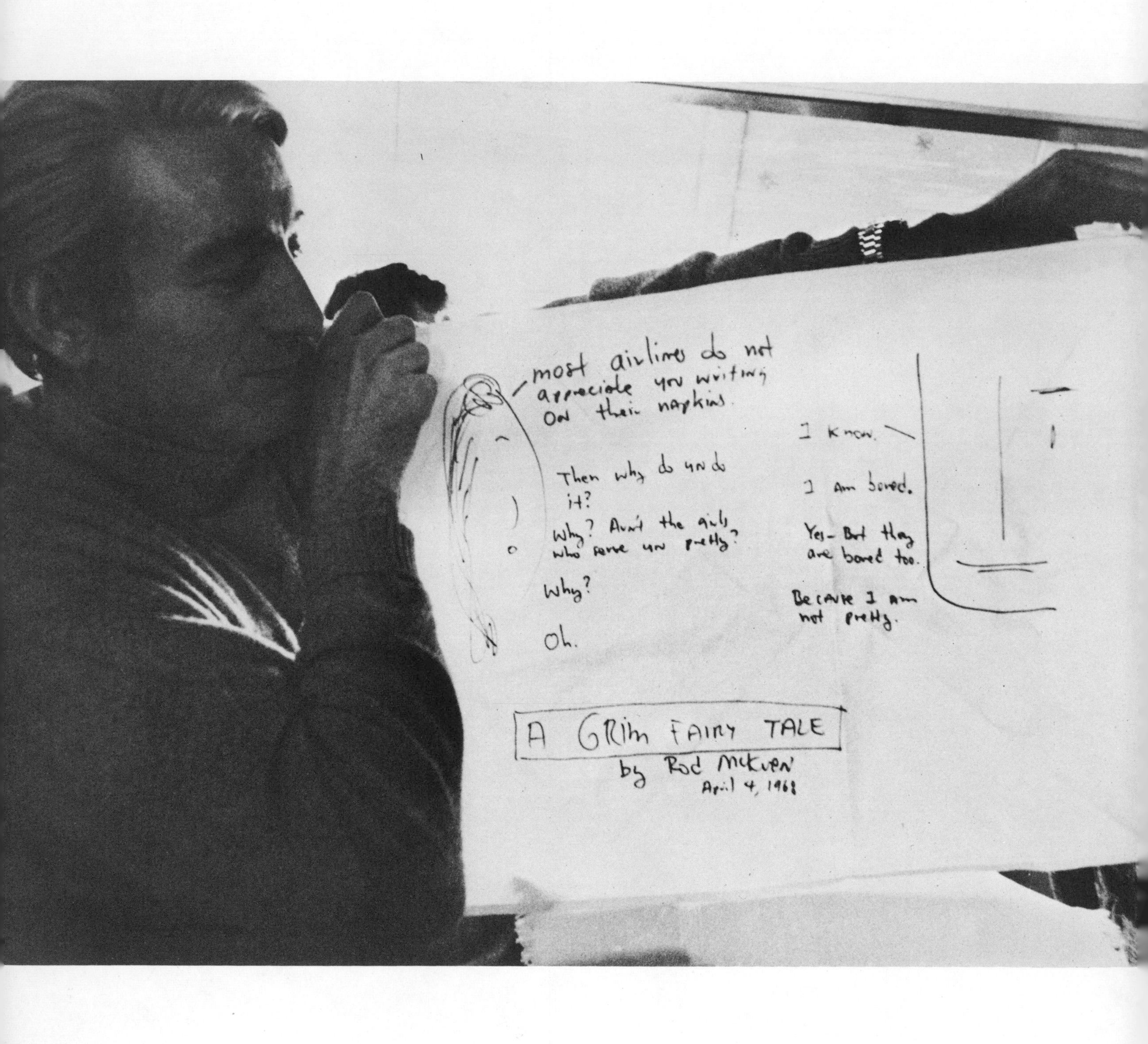
most airlines do not appreciate you writing on their napkins.
I know.
Then why do you do it?
I am bored.
Why? Aren't the girls who serve you pretty?
Yes— But they are bored too.
Why?
Because I am not pretty.
Oh.
A GRIM FAIRY TALE
by Rod McKuen
April 4, 1968

Methinks Thou Doth Protest Too Much

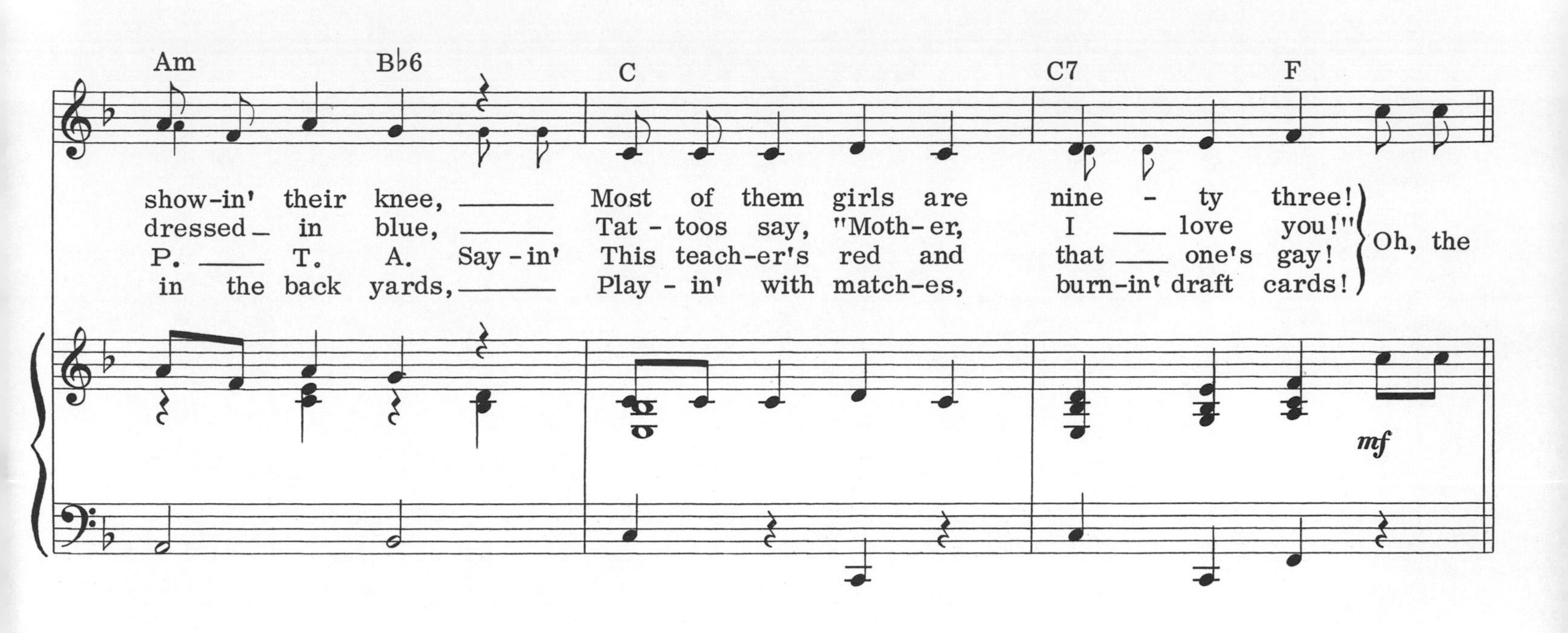
Am
Bb6
C
C7
F
show-in' their knee, Most of them girls are nine - ty three!
dressed in blue, Tat - toos say, "Moth-er, I love you!"
P. T. A. Say-in' This teach-er's red and that one's gay!
in the back yards, Play - in' with match-es, burn-in' draft cards!
Oh, the
mf
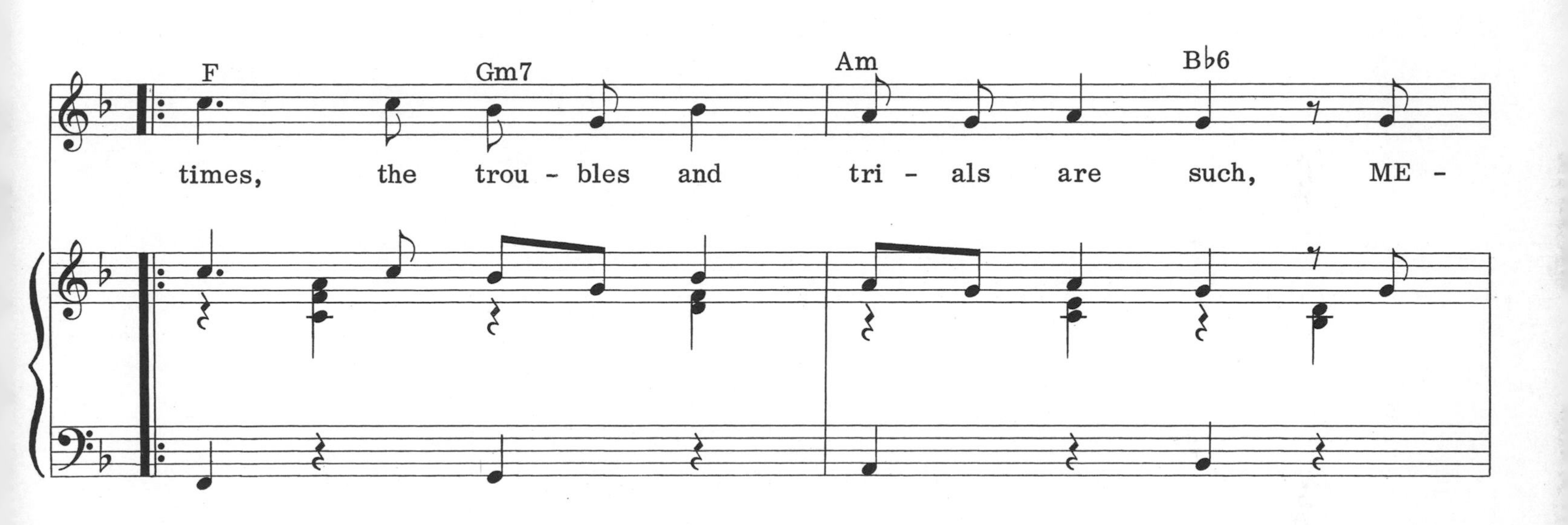
F
Gm7
Am
Bb6
times, the trou - bles and tri - als are such, ME -
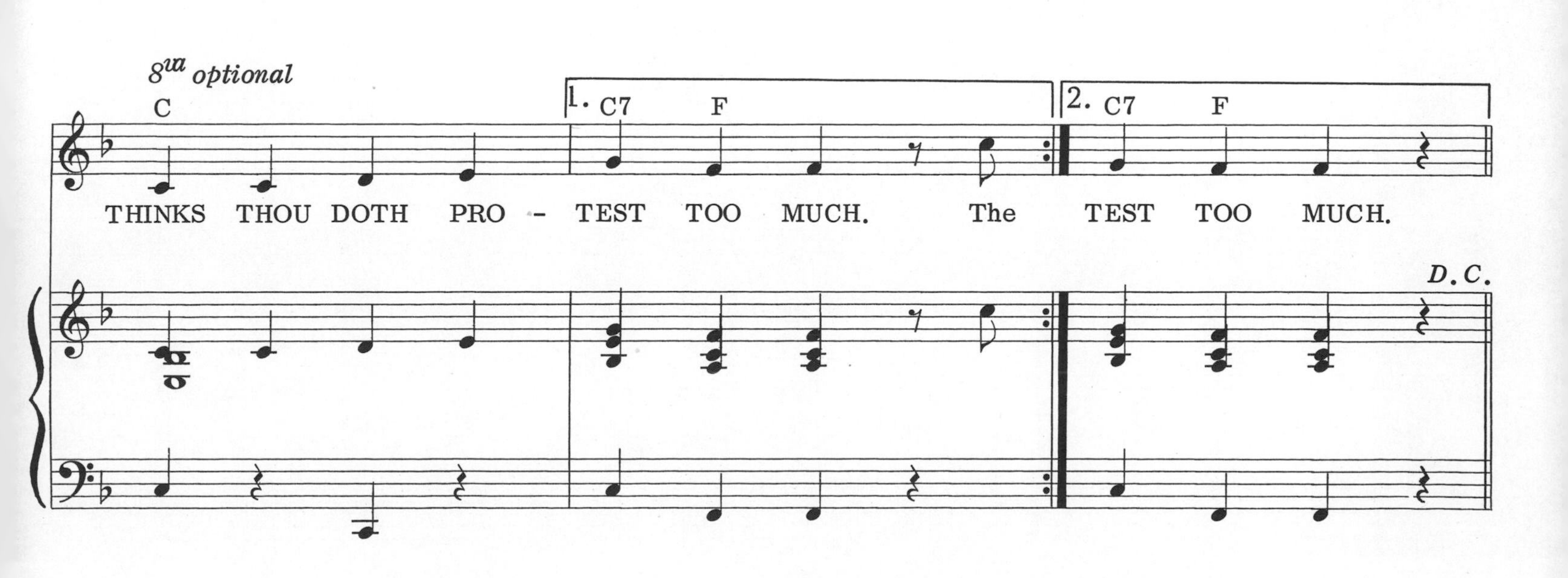
8va optional
C
1. C7
F
2. C7
F
THINKS THOU DOTH PRO - TEST TOO MUCH. The TEST TOO MUCH.
D.C.

Second Best

Slowly, with feeling
C
Am
Dm7
G7(♭9)
C
I want-ed the moon,
but set-tl'd for or-ang-es,
I looked for the rain and
mp
Am7
Dm7
G7
Dm7
E7
found in - stead the dew.
I want-ed the sea to
Em7
Am7
Dm7
G7
Dm7
E♭maj7
car-ry me home,
But it swept me a - long with the tide.
Dm7
G7
C
G7(♭9)
Am
Dm7
E7
Am7
While look-ing for stars to hold in my hand,

Dm7
G7sus
G7
Dm7
E7(+9)
I found to my great sur-prise,
They nev - er come out of the
Am7
Bb6
E7
Am7
Dm7
Dm7(b5)
G7sus
G7
heav - ens to shine in peo-ple's eyes.
Dm7
E7
Em7
Am7
Dm7
E7
Am
I tried for the top, but like all the rest, I fi - n'ly set - tled
Bb
G7
Cmaj7
for SEC - OND BEST.
R.H.

Something Beyond

Ab6 Gm7 Fm7 Eb6 Db9 C9 F7(+5) Bb9
thir - ty - third of A - pril and the for-ty-first of May. It well may
Gm7 Fm7 Eb G+ Ab Bb7
be I'll nev - er come to see the se - cret se-crets on the dark - er side of
Gm7 Bbm7 Ab Bb7 Eb Db Db9
me; But I'll keep look - ing 'til the need to look is gone, My arms reach
G7(+5) Cm7 F7 Emaj7 Eb
out to - ward SOME-THING BE - YOND.
3
3

The Way It Was Before

Eb Eb9 Ab Bb7 Cm G7 Cm7
words; And a friend was a friend and a lov - er was a lov - er; And
Ab Ebmaj7 Cm7 Fm7 Bb7 Eb Fm7
when you prayed to God, you felt He real - ly heard. The flow - ers all are dy - ing. The
Bb9 Ebmaj7 Eb Fm7
kites are sail - ing down, I guess the friend - ly an - i - mals have
Eb7 Eb Ab Gm Fm7 Ebmaj7
come a - long and gone; I used to wait for sum - mer, but sum - mer comes no more, And I
Eb Cm7 Fm7 Bb7 Eb
wish it was THE WAY IT WAS BE - FORE.
rall.

The Hunters

for Lee Mendelson
Moderato
G7 C Dm G7 C G7
THE HUNT-ERS come, THE HUNT-ERS go down dark streets
mf
C G7 C Dm7 G7
danc - ing to the on - ly tunes they know; And
F C G7 C
like the does in morn - ing that feed a - long the lake,
G7 Dm7 G7 C tacet
Hearts are on - ly un - der - brush be-neath their feet that break. Don't wor-ry the

Dm7
G7
C
F
wind, did-n't you know, When the morn-ing
C
G7
comes, they'll go.
THE HUNT-ERS
smile
Dm7
va-cant smiles,
And the
prom - is - es they make are on - ly good a lit - tle while;
For the

F
C
G7
C
hunt - er and the hunt - ed are real - ly quite the same, And the
G7
Dm7
G7
C
tacet
hunt-ing, not the lov - ing, is the pleas-ure of the game. Don't wor-ry the
Dm7
G7
C
F
wind, did'-nt you know, When the morn-ing
C
G7
C
C7
F
G7
comes, they'll go.
1. Fly, bird, they're com-ing and they'll
2. Run, lone -some li - on, don't be

C G7 C Em F G7
catch you if they can, — Lit-tle — fox, you're not so cun-ning,—
caught, — fright-ened doe, They aim their ar - rows straight — and — they'll
Dm7 G7 C G7 C G7 C G7 C G7
You can't fool the man.
cut you down and go.
THE HUNT-ERS
THE HUNT-ERS
C Dm7 G7 C G7 C G7
turn, THE HUNT-ERS stare, — They would have us all be-
come, THE HUNT-ERS go down dark streets danc-ing to the
C Dm7 G7 F
liev - ing — they've real - ly come to care; — But just a-cross our
on - ly tunes they know; And the hunt is not for

C
G7
C
shoul-der they sight an-oth-er doe, They quick-ly make their
pleas-ure, for the pleas-ure's in the pain, And you should-n't be out
G7
Dm7
G7
C
(tacet)
Dm7
kill, as they turn their backs to go.
walk-ing, for the hunt-er comes a-gain.
Don't wor-ry the wind,
G7
C
F
did-n't you know, When the morn-ing
comes, they'll go.

About the Author

Rod McKuen was born in Oakland, California, at the end of the Depression. He grew up in California, Nevada, Washington, and Oregon, and worked as a laborer, stunt man, radio disk jockey, and newspaper columnist before serving in the Army in Japan and Korea as a psychological-warfare scriptwriter; he was a member of the Korean Civil Assistance Command.

After he returned home Mr. McKuen was encouraged by his friend Phyllis Diller to perform at San Francisco's Purple Onion. During the engagement he was brought to Hollywood and put under contract to Universal-International as an actor. In 1959 he moved to New York to compose and conduct the music for Albert McCleery's highly lauded television series *The CBS Workshop*.

Mr. McKuen has played the major cabarets and concert halls of the world, and has written more than seven hundred songs. His material has been performed by the leading entertainers and recording artists the world over. Mr. McKuen spends seven months of the year in a house in the Hollywood hills, with a menagerie of cats and dogs, where he does most of his writing. The balance of his time he devotes to traveling and performing in Europe.

With the publication of *Stanyan Street and Other Sorrows* in 1966 and *Listen to the Warm* a year later, Mr. McKuen became the best-selling poet in America. He is currently writing screenplays for both books, and his third volume of poetry, *Lonesome Cities,* has just been published.